D1645813
Santiago de Compostela told to children
Text Ana Sánchez and Marta Marín
Drawings Pilarín Bayés de Luna
Ediciones Miguel Sánchez

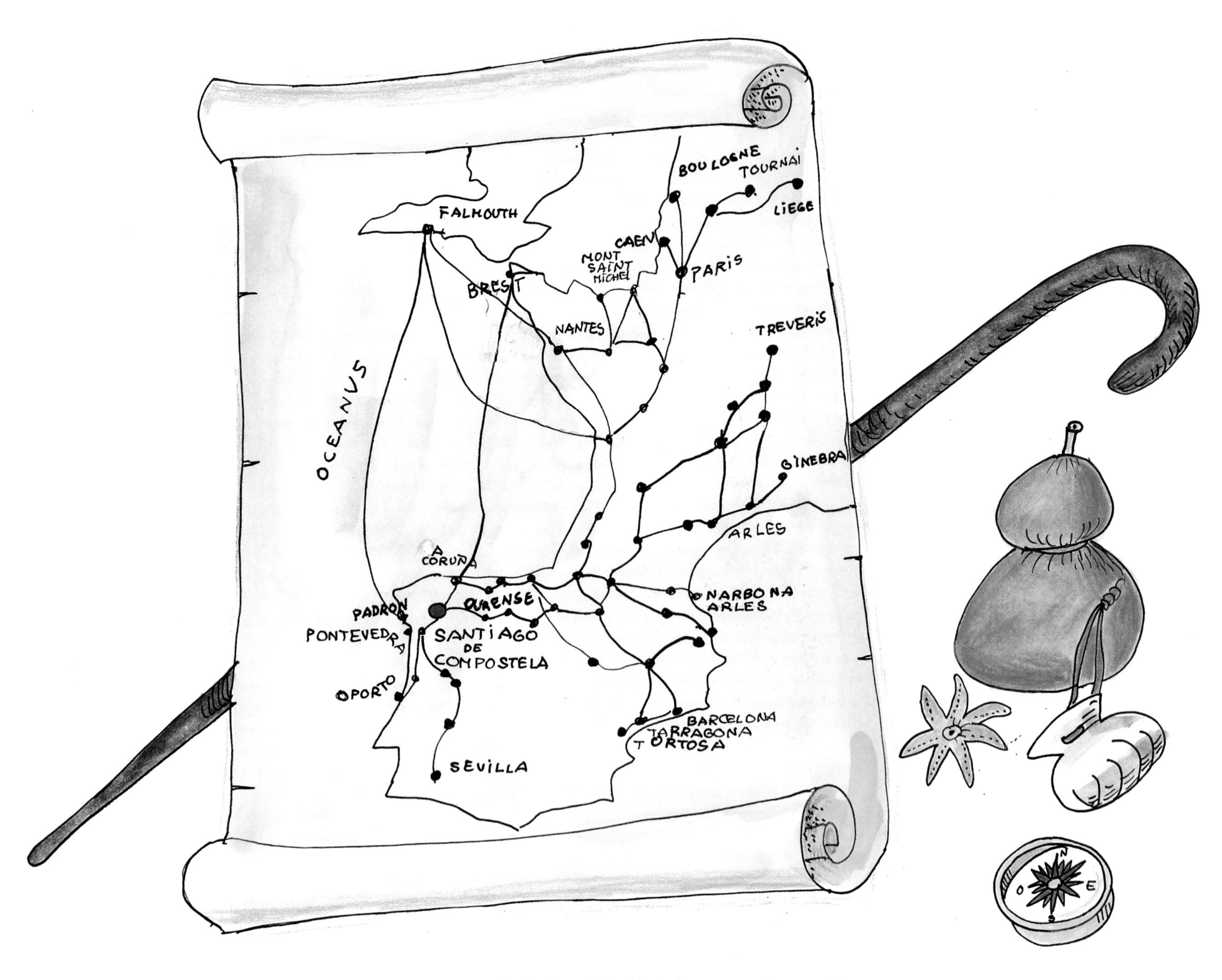

Our thanks to Simón Vicente López, Julio Prado and José Luis Serrano, authors and illustrator of "Compostela una historia entretenida"; to the authors of "Historia de la ciudad de Santiago de Compostela" and its coordinator Ermelindo Portela; to Celalba Rivera, Jaime Maroño, Ramón Izquierdo, the Couceiro family, Enrique and Alfredo González, to the Parador de los Reyes Católicos and to the Consortium of Santiago.

Heartfelt regards to Flora Fernández de Gándara, Galician great-grandmother of Pilarín and to our uncle Ángel Peinado, Kapellmeister of Granada Cathedral, musician and composer who put Rosalía's poems to music.

Translation by: Adam Cundy (STU-Traductores, s.l.) • *Prepress*: Paperlitos • *Photocomposition and layout*: Susana Martínez Ballesteros

Printing: Gráficas la Madraza • *I.S.B.N.*: 978-84-7169-145-3 • *Legal deposit*: GR-1.321/2014

A thousand travellers passed through its walls, pilgrims from all around arrived in Santiago attracted by the stories and legends that the people told. Wise women, elves, craftsman, clerics, merchants and nobles inhabited a city that many believed was magic. They say that there was no city like it in the world. Nobody could have imagined what happened one day…

Pablo and Maria have travelled to Santiago de Compostela with their parents. They don't yet know that they

are going to become involved in one of the most fantastic stories ever to unfold in this city.

The whole family, after enjoying the day, are walking towards the city centre.

"Why are there so many shells on the ground? They're like giant clams!"

"They're great scallop shells, a mollusc from the seas of Galicia" answers father. In the past, pilgrims would buy them as a souvenir at the end of their journey. They indicated the route of the path to Santiago."

"Pilgrims?..." whispered the children.

On seeing their faces mother says:

"This city has a history of legends. Tradition tells of some fantastic and miraculous events. The tomb of James the Apostle, a disciple of Jesus of Nazareth was discovered here, a long time ago, in the 9th century. At the beginning of the Middle Ages, when it happened there weren't any buildings.

"Wasn't there anything?"

"There was only a forest that hid an ancient cemetery", responded mother and continued.

"It's said that a hermit, Pelayo, lived alone in the area and one night saw some strange lights in the forest. So, he told the area's bishop. Teodomiro (that was the bishop's name) discovered a magnificent tomb there: "They're the remains of Santiago the Apostle!" he said. He quickly informed the king of Asturias, Alfonso II, who ordered a church to be built there. He also founded a monastery so that the monks would look after the relics. The news spread like wildfire and little by little people started to arrive on pilgrimages from many places to worship Santiago."

"On pilgrimages?"

"Pilgrimages were journeys that were made to the tomb of a saint to ask for help" explained father, "and the one for Santiago was very famous in Europe. The route followed by the first pilgrims is the famous "Way of Saint James".

"To attend to the pilgrims" continued mother, "craftsman and merchants such as shoemakers, tailors, silversmiths, bakers and butchers started to settle here, as well as lots of priests. Around

that small sanctuary they built houses, monasteries, churches and hospitals... And in that way a real city was formed.

"This city?" asked Maria.

"Well obviously!" said her brother.

They went further in along the calle de San Pedro. The people they came across seemed sad. In the doors of the houses, groups of men and women were speaking heatedly in a language they didn't understand.

"They're very worried and they're speaking in Galician" said the father.

"In Galician?"

"Yes, a very old language that is spoken in Galicia."

The parents tried to work out why the people were so agitated and asked a group of backpackers what was happening there.

"You don't know? Something extraordinary has happened. There's no music in Santiago!"

"But how is it possible?" exclaimed mother.

"They can't ring the bells, and the musical instruments can't sound, and the people can't sing either! Inside the Cathedral, we've seen some bagpipe players try in vain to make their bagpipes sound. It's like magic!"

The family were astonished. Why would this happen?

They got to a crossroads and stopped at a stall where a woman was selling natural drinks.

"Four apple juices please" said mother.

The woman looked at Pablo and Maria. "Those

children could break the spell on the city!", she thought.

"Do you want to help make the music return?" she asked them.

They nodded and so she put some drops of a magic potion in the juice. Its powers would connect them with the past.

Just above the juice stall Maria read: "*Rúa Porta do Camino*."

"Calle Puerta del Camino" clarified the woman. The pilgrims who arrived from France entered through here.

"Well I don't see any gate."

"Because there isn't one any more. Here was one of the gates of the wall that protected the city.

It was so well constructed that they called it Compostela (the well composed).

Minutes later, behind them Pablo and Maria hear:

"Clear the way please!" It was a family of peasants from the Middle Ages that had slipped through the time tunnel. "Only they can see it thanks to the magic drops in their drinks!" Meanwhile their parents, not paying attention, were looking at the "Royal Houses".

"Have you seen the Lord of Santiago's soldiers?" asked the peasant.

"We haven't seen any

soldiers" replied Pablo. "But where are you going in such a hurry? Who's the Lord of Santiago?"

"Oh my child!" We've come from *Sigueiro,* a village in the lands of the Lord Archbishop. If we manage to stay in Santiago for more than forty days without the lord claiming us, we'll be free" said the woman peasant. (In that time, only those who lived in the city enjoyed such a privilege).

"Aren't you free?"

"If only!" We're the Lord of Santiago's servants and we can't leave the village without his permission. He's lent us a small plot and in exchange we have to work his lands without rest" replied the peasant.

"My husband is a good carpenter and could open a craft workshop here. The children will be apprentices" said the woman.

The peasants said their goodbyes and asked them not to speak to anyone of the encounter.

"God will reward you for it!" and on saying that, they disappeared. Our friends looked at each other, incredulous.

In the Plaza de Cervantes the parents go into a bookshop near the Council building, the old town hall, while Maria and Pablo wait for them at the entrance. Suddenly, everything is changing around them. The buildings are becoming lower, they're not the same! Speechless, they see themselves surrounded by a never-ending hustle and bustle of strangely dressed people who

MIGUEL
DE
CERVANTES
SAAVEDRA
BANC

are buying and selling in numerous stalls in the plaza.

"Meat! Good beef!" shouted one.

"Who wants chicken? The best in Galicia!" yelled another.

"Flour, I've got recently milled flour!"

"What's happened?! Where are we?" asked Pablo, frightened

"You're in the *Praza do Campo*" replies a bread seller. "Where have you come from?" she asked on seeing how they were dressed.

Lost in thought, trying to work out what happened, they didn't answer.

"In the plaza del Campo!" said Pablo thoughtfully and immediately his demeanour changed. His face sparkled and, smiling, he said to his sister:

"We've travelled back in time! We're in the same plaza! Do you understand? It's because of the magic drink..."

Knowing that they had gone back in time (to the 12th century) they walked around the plaza. Next to Saint Benedict's Church they recognised the woman from the drinks stall selling medicinal plants. She was a *meiga*, a wise woman who on seeing them said:

"I was waiting for you to help you. I know why there's no music in Santiago. The spirit Alan is really angry and has cast a spell over the city."

"Why? What's happened to him?"

"Alan lives in a well by some ruins in the forest,

near here. Every night he leaves the well to sing and play the dulzaina with his companions. They're real music lovers. He's found out that they want to build tall buildings in his peaceful place and he's become furious with rage, because they will have to leave where they've lived for thousands of years. That's why there's no music in Santiago!"

"What can we do to calm him down?"

"I don't know anything else. Maybe here, in the plaza, someone can help you. Go carefully! Alan is watching. Ah! Buy the jet stone, it will be really useful to you.

The children said goodbye to the woman and approached a group of people crowding around a town crier.

"It is made known for whoever can understand: four words there will be, that up to heaven will take thee" he repeated over and over again.

"Bah! Words! Nobody can read here!" said the people, disappointed, moving away.

That message was for Pablo and Maria. They will have to make four words to break the spell. But how?

"Children!" Their parents' voices made them return to the present. "Let's continue along the Azabachería" proposed father. And they went along the street where in the past the workshops of the jet carvers were.

"Let's go in here!" said mother. It was a jet carver's workshop. All of the objects in the display cabinets were an intense black and very shiny. The children looked on with interest how the craftsman attempted to carve a cross out of a piece of black stone.

"That's jet?" asked Maria.

"Yes, the magic stone of Santiago."

"Magic? Does it have powers?" she insisted.

"Yes, this stone was very highly regarded not just for its beauty, but also because it was thought that it protected against bad omens. For the pilgrims it was a true talisman."

Seeing them so interested the jet carver said to them:

"Take this piece of jet, you will be able to see for yourselves."

They'd hardly left the shop when a violent wind started to blow so hard that they were lifted off the floor and taken in the opposite direction.

Pablo remembered the words of the wise woman and thought that it was the work of the spirit. He clenched the piece of jet between his hand and it started to shine so brightly that its flashes resisted the force of the wind. In a few seconds they had been transported to the Casa de la Troya, but Pablo and Maria returned to meet their parents as if nothing had happened.

Now in the Plaza de la Inmaculada, some young musicians tried in vain to make their violins heard next to the door of the Cathedral, and the bagpipers in the Passage blew and blew into their bagpipes with no success. Lots of people grouped round them on realising that not one musical note could be heard.

In the crowd, the children saw a man dressed strangely, almost ragged, heading towards a large building on the other side of the plaza. They followed him and entered the guest quarters of the Monastery of Saint Martin Pinario.

From the hall, they heard the conversation that the man was having with a monk from the monastery:

"God protect you. Where have you come from?"

"I've walked from Paris and suffered many hardships along the way."

"You're lucky. Today is the day of the Apostle." It was the 25th of July 1292.

"Here" said the monk as he gave him a large loaf of bread, cheese and some coins. "You know that we look after pilgrims here. Before entering the Cathedral, wash yourself in the Fountain of Paradise and in the same plaza you can buy yourself some new shoes."

As he was leaving, the pilgrim said to the children "Find the symbol of the hospital!"

The parents are waiting for them to take a family photo in front of the great door of the monastery.

"Look at the sculpture of Saint Martin sharing his cape with a beggar" says their mother.

Looking up they saw something become detached from the cape and fall to the floor. It was a piece of cloth with a letter.

"It's a P! The first clue!" said Pablo putting it in his pocket, and they continued walking.

They immediately came to an enormous plaza. Pablo and Maria started running towards a building with a big shiny chain in front of its façade. There was an opening and they went in. They rubbed their eyes. A strangely dressed young boy shouted:

"Hey! Hey! Hurry up and come in! This is royal territory and the Lord of Santiago doesn't rule here. You're safe! I also had a problem. A shell seller accused me of stealing some shells from him. If I hadn't taken shelter here I would have been arrested. I'm now working as an assistant in the Hospital apothecary. And you, who's after you?"

"Us? No one! We're just going to rest a little in the hotel.

"But this is a hospital! The hospital of the Catholic Monarchs. Look at Fernando and Isabel on those medallions. They've ordered its construction for the poor and sick pilgrims who come to Santiago. There are so many of them, and from so many countries!... That's why they entrusted the project to their faithful architect, Enrique Egas, one of the best.

"It's really big!"

"The biggest and best in the city. You can see for yourselves." And he disappeared through the door.

The parents were admiring the beautiful plateresque facade of the Hostal, complete with decorative details such as the objects of silversmiths.

"For nearly five hundred years this hotel was a hospital" their father tells them.

"We already know that!"

With faces like a daydreaming emoticon the parents go to the cafeteria. Meanwhile, Pablo and Maria, wandering round, enter an inviting room, the Hall of Saint Mark. Suddenly, the room transforms and the young boy appears at the entrance, between shelves full of ceramic jars, funnels, boxes and stills.

"What are you doing here, in the apothecary? Is something hurting you? You'll have to wait. The apothecary is upstairs, in the men's infirmary, visiting the patients with the doctor. Then he'll go to the medicinal garden. We've run out of mallow for poultices."

"Poul...what..?"

"Ah! The apothecary is like a pharmacy!" said Pablo. "But we don't want medicine, we want to find the symbol of the Hospital".

"Easy!" Right here in the Apothecary Courtyard. They also call it the patio of Saint Mark, but take care not to trip over the people!"

Pablo and Maria went out but didn't see anyone.

"Look, animal heads!" exclaimed Maria, pointing at the gargoyles.

"And those shields? Are they the ones from the hospital?"

"No! Up there! In the windows! Do you see?"

"Yes! There's a cross in a circle!"

At that moment, the jet shined again. They heard a harsh noise, as if someone was coughing. Turning their heads round they were surprised to see the gargoyle of a monk who appeared to be choking and with a sudden cough spat out something that fell onto the floor.

"Two badges with the letter L!" they exclaimed, and ran to look for their parents.

"Where were you?" scolded mother "we're going to visit the Chapel and the Courtyards.

They passed the renaissance Courtyard of Saint Mark, which they already knew.

Entering the Chapel, the most important and beautiful place in the hospital, at the crosspiece their mother asked them to look at the rooms on the upper floor.

From there the sick, lying in their beds, attended mass" she told them.

"But it's a dining room!" exclaimed Maria.

"Of course, because it's a hotel now!" replied Pablo.

The children laughed and continued the visit with their parents to the rest of the Courtyards. In the Courtyard of Saint John, father, reading an information panel, said:

"So many people lived here! The sick, doctors, priests, pharmacists, and cooks, gardeners, carpenters, tinkers, dressmakers... almost a city!"

"It even had a prison..." mother insisted.

"A prison!" exclaimed the children.

"Yes, and the great kitchen was also here. Upstairs on the top floor were the infirmaries and on the ground floor the rooms where pilgrims were taken in. In the right wing the women were treated and on left the men" father continued.

"How curious! The sick shared the beds. Each mattress was occupied by two patients" said mother.

"Two patients to a bed?" asked Maria.

"Then the hospitals weren't like they are now. The mattresses were made of straw and there weren't any washing machines. The washer women hand-washed the sheets and the patients' nightgowns and had to boil the clothes of the infectious to disinfect them.

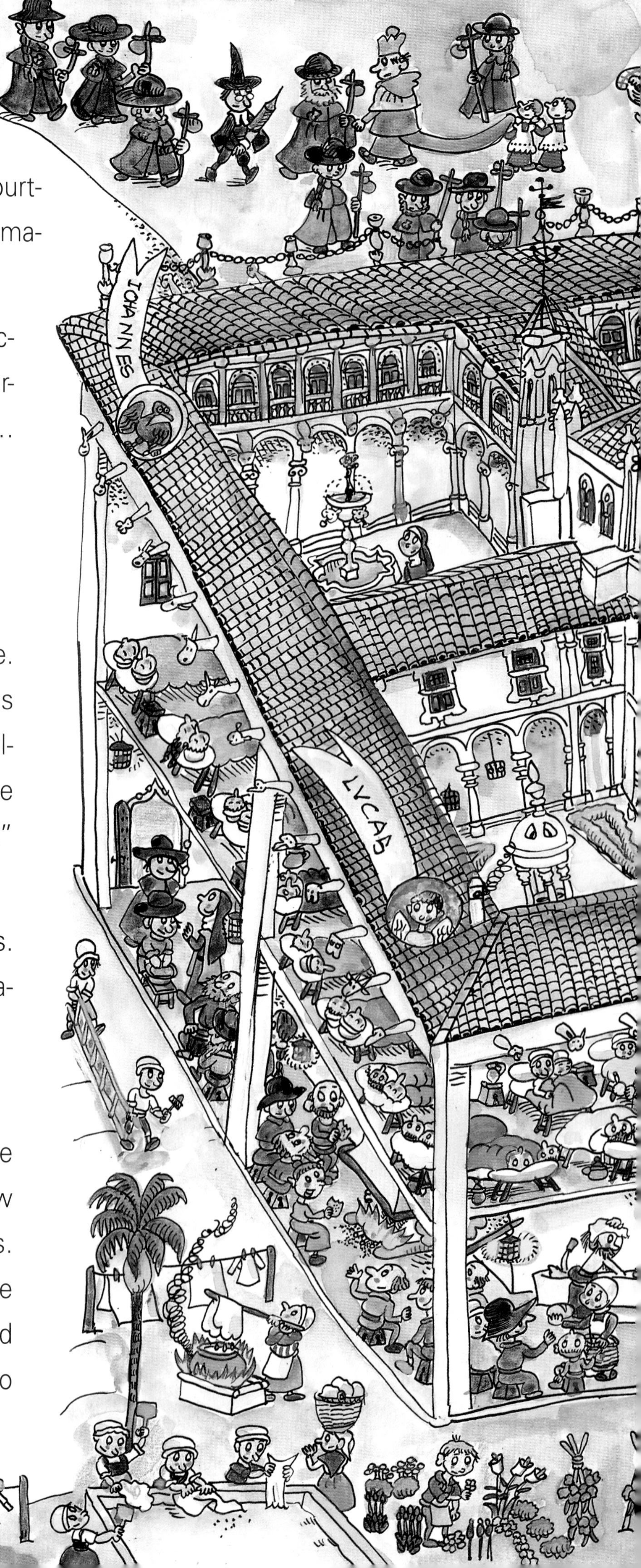

All these stories were bubbling around Pablo and Maria's imaginations when they saw their friend again, the assistant from the Hospital apothecary, who was running hastily. Where would he be going?...

The visit was coming to an end. At reception, the family crosses a group of people and heard the receptionist say:

"You're in luck, there's still room". They had arrived in time to enjoy one of the three daily free meals that the Hotel continues to offer to pilgrims.

ARQUITECTUS
MA
XI
MVS
LONDON
NANTES
PARIS
HAMBURG
BILBAO
SANTIAGO
LEON

Leaving the Plaza del *Obradoiro*, the jet stone started to shine intensely. What was it telling them?

They looked to their left and…oh! A bishop, flanked by soldiers, was talking with some priests. They had gone back in time again!

"Look, there it says Gelmírez Palace" observed Maria.

"Well that must be the Lord of the city" said Pablo seeing the soldiers in his entourage. Listen!"

"How the city has improved thanks to you, archbishop Gelmírez!" The cathedral is almost finished" said one of the priests.

"Yes, the works have advanced a lot. I've brought one of the best masters in the art of cathedral building in Europe. It's essential to take in so many pilgrims!"

"And what can be said of the new churches, the *rúa Nuova* and the water channelled to the fountains!" said another excitedly.

"However, the citizens of Santiago have rebelled against their lord's power. How ungrateful! They even set fire to the cathedral. Do you remember?" said a third.

Gelmírez, before entering the palace, threw some coins on the floor for the beggars. He did it with such skill that one fell at the feet of Pablo who on picking it up discovered… the letter G!

"Quick, children!" called father, and the family joined a tourist guide group about to visit the Cathedral.

"The Cathedral of Santiago was built between the 11th and 13th century, above all in the era of archbishop Gelmírez and there was a period when it was protected by battlements, like a castle, because the bishops, who were feudal lords with lots of power, had serious conflicts with the citizens and nobles of the Lands of Santiago.

"And where are the battlements?" asked Pablo.

"You can't see them from here. There are some left, but you have to climb the roof to see them" responded the guide and continued.

"Later, in the 18th century, a new decoration hid the first Romanesque church. The Archbishop and cathedral council employed Fernando de Casas y Novoa to construct this grand façade in a baroque style. Can you see how overloaded with ornaments it is and how many curved lines it has?" he asked them.

"Yes, there are some giant spirals up there" replied Maria.

"And that lord wore a hat like a pilgrim's, do you see it? said Pablo to his sister.

"He's James the Apostle, the Patron of Spain" replied the guide and continued explaining.

In that era the archbishops of Santiago, the cathedral and the monasteries had a lot of riches. Because of that, as well as attending to the poor and the pilgrims, they dedicated part of their money to making the city bigger constructing and renovating buildings. The workshops of the stonemasons who worked the granite stones were in this plaza, which is where it got its name, *Obradoiro*" he said, going towards the entrance.

At that moment, a girl falls off her bicycle. Pablo and María rush to help her. Surprise! Scattered on the ground there were three pieces of stone with a carved O. They had found a new letter.

SEGLO XI-XII
CASAS-NOVOA

ATHEUS
TRIGONO
METRIA

Now in the Portico of Glory, everyone was entranced by the expressiveness and the stories that the stone figures told. Its architect, the master Mateo, had almost made them speak.

"There're so many musical instruments! and they're really strange!" said Maria, looking at the twenty-four old men who crowned the tympanum of the central door.

"It's a representation of Glory, which for Christians is the paradise where good people will live in peace with god at the end of their days" their father explained to them.

"There's music in Glory!" whispered Pablo into his sister's ear.

They saw Santiago in the column of the mullion and just behind, moving over the threshold, a man hitting his head against a kneeling statue.

"For the Galician people this is Saint "dos Croques" or Saint of Bumps on the head. According to the legend, if you hit your head three times on his you will increase your intelligence. They say it's the master Mateo" said the guide.

Inside, an imposing silence surrounded the air. There wasn't any music in the cathedral either!

"It's a real shame!" exclaimed the guide "Music had always caressed those walls where choruses of pilgrims from all countries, accompanied by instruments, sang praise to God" he said, describing to them the Codex Calixtinus, a medieval manuscript preserved in the Cathedral Museum.

Once inside, the children were surprised by the height of the columns. They seemed gigantic!

"It's so big!" "Is that why it's called a cathedral?" Maria asked her parents.

"It's called that because here is the seat or dignity of the bishop" explained mother.

"Look! There's a floor up there!" observed Pablo.

"That's the gallery. That's where the pilgrims rested and attended the religious celebrations" said the guide, hearing him.

"They took a long time to construct this cathedral, almost a century and a half."

"That long?"

"Yes, it wasn't easy to build such a big stone building. That's why various architects participated in its construction: Bernardo the Old, Master Esteban, Bernardo the Young and the Master Mateo. So they were called Master stonemasons and came with a team that formed their workshop and worked at their orders.

With interest the group followed the explanations on the construction of the Romanesque temple, the half-barrel crypt, the wide naves, and the ambulatory surrounding the great altar to ease the passage of the pilgrims towards the place of the relics. They also saw how the naves met and formed a cross.

"How odd!" said Maria.

"They did it like that to represent Jesus on the cross" explained the guide.

"What's that?" asked Pablo, puzzled to see some very strange signs on the columns.

"Ah! That's the mark of the stonemason who sculpted the stone. They signed their pieces like that so they would get paid for their work. There are lots more, but you can't always see them."

At the cross, whilst the guide explained that the first great altar in the Romanesque style was made of silver and was substituted for the current one in the Baroque style, Pablo and Maria, who seemed distracted, asked:

"What are these trumpets?"

"They're organ pipes, a musical instrument. It's from the 18th century and the organist makes it sound with a keyboard. But it's not working today."

Following the tradition, the family joined the line of people ready to embrace the image of Saint James. Then they went down to the crypt. Impulsively, Pablo and Maria rubbed their eyes. A pilgrim, dressed in an old fashioned way, prayed while kneeling before the relic.

"It's the pilgrim of Saint Martin Pinario!"

"Shhh!" their mother made them be quiet.

When they walked past it, the jet shined again. The pilgrim opened his hand and dropped two pieces of parchment with a drawing. It was the letter R, written with complicated coloured lines.

"They're really strange" said Maria when she saw the letters that were similar to those in the Codex Calixtinus.

"Quick! Come and see the *botafumeiro*! The *tiraboleiros* are going to make it work." The guide was talking to them in a low voice:

Do you see that gigantic censer? It's a brazier where incense is burnt to perfume the atmosphere. In the Middle Ages thousands of pilgrims arrived without having washed during the journey and incense is a very aromatic substance that purifies the air. Can't you smell it?"

Maria and Pablo observed captivated how the contraption swung from side to side, getting faster each time.

"It's going to touch the ceiling!" exclaimed Maria.

When the *tiraboleiros* finished, the jet shone again and on passing them one of them said:

"They told me to give you this."

"They're two letters the same! The L!" The pilgrim turned round and looked at them.

The guide continued explaining: "This is the Puerta de Platerías where the pilgrims left the Cathedral happy to have been pardoned. It's called that because it provided access to the silversmith quarter.

Our friends were the first to leave and their parents were puzzled to see them whispering.

Outside on the facade of the Door the group admired the tales of the life of Christ sculpted in stone to teach people who couldn't read or write.

"Look, lions!" exclaimed Pablo.

"Yes, they're the guardians of the temple" responded the guide. "Can't you see more animals?"

"The monkeys!" shouted Maria.

"Monkeys signify evil and they're provoking Jesus" he said and continued.

"Do you see that building with balconies? It's the Casa de Cabildo. But although it looks like one, it isn't a casa."

"What is it?"

"It's just a beautiful facade that the cathedral chapter ordered to be built to make the plaza beautiful."

Then they went to the Quintana, an adjacent plaza, where they were shown the Clock Tower and the Holy Gate that is only opened when the fiesta of Santiago falls on a Sunday.

The clock bell couldn't ring the passing of the hours either. The people of Santiago are afraid.

The guide finished and, bidding them good day, said goodbye.

There was a stage in the plaza and, next to the walls of the Monastery of Antealteres, a music group was having a heated discussion.

"The Town Council should solve the problem! We can't give the concert tonight!" protested one.

"We're looking for a solution, but nothing like this has ever happened before!" replied the municipal official.

Pablo and Maria had to hurry, only they knew what was happening. They went back with their parents to the Plaza de Platerías, which was very animated. You can still see shops that sell silver jewels and shells today.

OBRADOIRO
QUINTANA
PLATERÍAS
RUA DO FRANCO
RUA DO VILAR
RUA NOVA
CAL

Seeing a numerous group of people with rucksacks Pablo asked:

"Why are there so many people?"

"Because they've completed the journey like the old pilgrims and there, in the Casa del Dean, they receive the Compostelana" answered their mother.

"Dean...? Compostelana...?"

"The Dean is a very important person in the cathedral government and the Compostelana is a document that is given to those who have done the journey.

In the plaza again, surprise! The wise woman was there with her drinks stall and when they were passing her she said in a low voice:

"Look for the shield with the five stars and give it to his lordship! Over there!" she indicated, pointing towards the *rúa do Franco*, where some students were chatting exitedly.

"Can we help you?" "We're looking for a shield with five stars."

"It's right here, in the Fonseca Palace, in the University. Look up!"

"A shield with five stars...!

"Can you give us paper and a pencil?"

Pablo quickly drew the shield.

"It's the emblem of the archbishop Alonso de Fonseca III" said the student. "He founded the University over five hundred years ago. They say he was very powerful and cultured".

"Do you know where we can find him?"

"Well, he died a long time ago, but there inside, in the courtyard, there's a statue of him."

"Look! There he is!
How thoughtful" said Maria.

"Here, your shield" Pablo said to the statue. "Will you give us a clue for our puzzle?"

"Yes, but you have to listen to me first. I haven't spoken to anyone for a long time! I ordered this palace to be built. I made the great architect Rodrigo Gil de Hontañón come. What a beautiful cloister!"

The children were worried, but lord Fonseca III continued:

"The classrooms surrounded the courtyard. What a hustle and bustle of students and teachers! Now everything is quieter. There are no classes now. This palace became too small for them. They say that today there are more than twenty-five thousand students. Now it's the University Library.

They looked all about them.

"I'm finishing. The student music group is at the gate. Watch the tambourine player's cape and... Good luck!"

GIL
ONTAÑON
COPER-
NICUS

When they are leaving the student musicians are perplexed. Their instruments don't play! Neither guitars, nor bandurrias, nothing! Stealthily they approach the one with the tambourine and take a card attached to one of his multicoloured belts.

The letter T!

It was time to get their energy back. They were in an area of bars, restaurants and shops: the streets of *do Vilar* and *do Franco*, pretty arcades and stone houses. The name comes from the first settlers in medieval times, the Galician villagers and the Franks who established their businesses there. They built their homes, small and modest, in muddy streets. Balconies and projections stuck out over columns forming the first arcades.

Later, in the Baroque era, stone mansions for the nobles were erected and Council bylaws improved the health and beauty of these "rúas" that were gradually taking on their current image.

The family went in to a restaurant ready to enjoy some typical Galician dishes. While they ate a piece of pie, Pablo and Maria spoke amongst clues. Suddenly, Maria found a small ceramic plaque under her plate.

"It's an E!" she said showing it to her brother.

"Yes, but we have to make four words to break the spell over the city."

The restaurant owner's children, Anton and Iria, who had been watching, heard them. They also wanted to solve the puzzle! They spoke with Pablo and Maria and, with their parents' permission, they arranged to meet later in the plaza del Obradoiro.

"Let's go to the Tourist Information Office" suggested their father. They were very close.

"The Goose game!" exclaimed Pablo.

"This game was the guide that orientated the old pilgrims on the path to Santiago de Compostela" explained the girl at the information office.

The parents bought it and when the children started to examine it, the labyrinth square opened! It had the letter D stuck behind it.

"We've got another one!" they exclaimed and left.

"There're some gardens near here" said mother looking at the map.

On the way to towards the park, in the plaza del *Toural*, Pablo and Maria felt a sudden burning in their eyes and, when they rubbed them, they went back to the past. They were in the 18th century. A cart pulled by oxen had stopped outside the gate of a palace where a group of servants were talking with the cart driver:

"Quick, unload! The Marquis of Bendaña is about to arrive!" said a servant to the porters.

"I bring wine, wheat and chestnuts from the lands of the lord marquis in Touro. But there, at the gate of the wall, in Mazarelos, they arrested me and made me pay to enter the city. Curses!" protested the cart driver.

"But look at the beautiful country house that the lord has just built. The most beautiful in all Santiago!" replied the servant.

It was the year 1760 and the nobles liked luxury and urban life. Amongst the hustle and bustle, various chestnuts rolled on the floor. The jet shone and Pablo and Maria rushed to grab them. There was a white one with a scrawl: The letter A! At once they put it away and heard the voices of their parents calling them.

The Alameda Park seemed enormous. Pablo and Maria looked around while their parents rested.

"Hey! Hey!" someone was calling them. But there was nobody there, just a big sculpture. They read the inscription: "Galicia a Rosalia de Castro. Insigne poetisa".

"It's her who's speaking!"

"Look there, at my feet" indicated Rosalia.

They crouched down and picked up a tiny book.

"It's a music book! *Good-bye, ri-vers; good-bye, foun-tains;*" said Maria reading under the musical notes.

"But it can't be sung!" insisted Rosalia. And saying that, a loose page came out of the book. The letter C!

Afterwards, the family went to the church of Saint Fiz de Solovio, where it is said that the hermit Pelayo lived, who their mother had told them about. Some black clouds forewarned of a storm and Pablo held the jet talisman tightly. At that instant, the brother and sister heard a warm voice:

"The spirit feels sorrow and rage" He won't hear the sounds of nature any more. Find the music that will soothe the anger!"

"Did you hear? Who could it be?"

"I don't know, but we have another clue" said Pablo and they walked towards the Plaza del *Obradoiro.*

Anton and Iria were waiting nervously on the Cathedral steps. When they

saw them Maria and Pablo started running. Suddenly a great storm broke.

"Let's go inside!" suggested Anton, who was the eldest.

The children, sitting on the floor, tried to form the four magic words.

"We have it!" exclaimed Pablo and Antón. They had formed the world p-o-r-t-i-c-o and they now had PÓRTICO DE LA GLORIA! Those were the four words! The could undo Alan's spell!

"What a shame! There's one missing!"

Pablo looked everywhere. He saw that the statue of the Apostle James was winking at him, at the same time as moving his head to one side. He got up like a shot and went through the door. Anton followed him. The jet was shining.

"Look! Above the *Santo dos Croques*!"

There was a piece of wood with a letter carved into it.

"The missing A!" and they ran to put it in its place.

Everyone there was able to see and hear it. It was incredible. The old stone instruments of the old men of the tympanum began to sound. The music calmed the spirit and filled the heart.

Such harmonic sounds soothed the spirit's rage. The storm ceased and the bells of Santiago started to chime. The musicians spread throughout the plazas, the student music group, the bagpipers, they all started to play rhythms and melodies on the instruments and an explosion of sound filled the air: guitars, violins, bagpipes, hand drums…

The parents were astonished. Their children had solved the city's problem!

The people went into the streets full of jubilation. They all went to the Obradoiro to celebrate. Music had returned to the city! But, why had it stopped? Only the four children knew the answer. Ah!... and that woman who, amongst the commotion, waved at them.